Revolutionary

Rebecca

The Liberty Belles Series
Book Three

Written by
Tracy Lawson

Illustrated by
Larissa Coriell

BOOKS

Columbus OH • Dallas TX
graylionbooks.com

ISBN-13: 979-8-9876123-3-0

Publisher's Cataloging-in-Publication data
Names: Lawson, Tracy, author. | Coriell, Larissa, author.
Title: Revolutionary Rebecca / by Tracy Lawson and Larissa Coriell.
Series: The Liberty Belles Series
Description: Columbus OH; Dallas TX: Gray Lion Books, 2023. | Summary:
Based on a true story of the American Revolution! In 1812, cousins Hess Alston
and Mary Pinkney learn how their grandmother Rebecca Motte relied on her
wits, courage, and a quiver full of arrows to contribute to the fight during the
British occupation of Charleston, South Carolina. The girls can't believe what
Rebecca was willing to sacrifice to help General Francis Marion capture a
British fort.
Identifiers: ISBN: 979-8-9876123-3-0 (paperback) | 979-8-9876123-4-7
(ebook)
Subjects: LCSH United States--History--Revolution, 1775-1783--Fiction. |
Siege of Charleston., 1780--Juvenile fiction. | Women--United States--History-
-18th century--Fiction. | BISAC JUVENILE FICTION / Historical / United
States / Colonial & Revolutionary Periods | JUVENILE FICTION /
Historical /United States / 19th Century | JUVENILE FICTION / Historical /
Military & Wars | JUVENILE FICTION /Girls & Women |
JUVENILE FICTION / Family / Multigenerational
Classification: LCC PZ7.1 .L39 Re 2024| DDC [Fic]--dc24

Author photos by Owen Jones and Larissa Coriell
Interior layout by Gray Lion Books
Cover illustration by Larissa Coriell
Cover design by Elizabeth Dunlap

Manufactured in the United States of America

This book is dedicated to
the descendants of
Rebecca Brewton Motte

Chapter 1

Eight-year-old Hess Alston sighed as she struggled with her tangled embroidery thread.

"I don't know how I can be expected to sew on such a beautiful day," she grumbled. "I'd rather be outside."

That morning in June 1812, she'd done battle with several stubborn knots and picked out nearly as many stitches as she'd put in her sampler.

Her cousin Mary Pinkney, who was a year older than Hess, didn't look up from threading her needle. "We *are* outside, silly. It's perfectly nice here on the porch."

Hess tossed her sampler on a chair and went to stand at the railing. The breeze rippled through the grass and bent the heads of thousands of yellow buttercups in the meadow at Eldorado, her uncle's plantation.

Years before, the girls' grandmother, Rebecca Motte, had named the plantation Eldorado, Spanish for 'City of Gold,' because of the flowers' vibrant color.

Right now, the sunshine, the breeze, and the flowers beckoned. "Come on, Mary! Let's go pick buttercups before it gets too hot."

"All right, if you want to." Mary carefully laid aside her own sampler and slowly followed Hess down the curving stairs to the lawn. Like many people who lived in the South Carolina low country, Mary always seemed to either be sick or recovering from some illness. She spent most of her time doing indoor things.

Hess, on the other hand, was hardly ever sick and loved being outdoors. With one hand on her straw hat to keep it from blowing away, she waited for her cousin to catch up, and together they waded into the tall grasses.

As they picked the yellow blossoms, Mary paused a few times to blot her forehead with her handkerchief. When a bead of sweat rolled down Hess's cheek, she wiped it away with her sleeve.

Hess looked up when their grandmother called from the porch, "Come have some lemonade, girls! You must be baking out in the heat."

Though she could have run across the lawn and up and down the stairs a dozen times without feeling tired, Hess walked with Mary back to the house. She climbed the stairs faster than her cousin even though she tried to slow down.

"Look, Grandma!" Hess ran across the porch and plopped down on the chair next to her grandmother's rocker.

"How lovely! Buttercups are my favorite flower." Mary sat on her other side and took off her sun hat. Grandma laid a hand on her perspiring forehead. "You didn't get too warm, did you, dear?"

"No, Grandma. I'm fine."

"All the same," Grandma tutted as she poured ice-cold lemonade into glasses. "You must be careful, Mary, not to get overtired."

Mary took a dainty sip and then picked up her sampler.

Hess laid her flowers in her lap, picked up her glass, and took a long, satisfying drink. She cast a glance at her sampler and sighed.

"Is something wrong with your needlework, Hess?" asked Grandma.

"No— " she paused, and then burst out, "Yes, there is! It's a tangled mess. Everyone expects me to like to sew. But I don't. A four-year-old can make neater stitches."

"You don't have to do everything the way others expect. That would be quite dull, wouldn't it?" Grandma reached for a quiver that hung on the back of her rocker.

The quiver was beautiful, with a design of flowers and swirls stamped into the leather and a fringe of cloth strips tied to the strap.

Grandma took out a slender pair of knitting needles and a ball of cotton thread. "Most people put their knitting in a basket, but I like to use this quiver instead."

Hess said, "I thought quivers were for arrows."

"A long time ago, it held arrows." Grandma set to work on the lace collar she was making. "It has plenty of room for my knitting, and I keep a few memories tucked in there as well."

"What kind of memories? Will you tell us a story?" Relieved that her grandmother wasn't going to make her work on her sampler, Hess began to weave her buttercups into a golden crown instead.

"Oh yes! Do tell us a story, Grandma!" said Mary.

"All right. The quiver reminds me of a time when I didn't do what people expected." Grandma brushed a sweaty wisp of Mary's blonde hair off her forehead. "Your mothers were a little older than you are now, when the arrows from this quiver helped win a battle in the war for independence."

Hess took off her sun hat and put the flower crown on her tangled auburn curls. "You fought the British soldiers with arrows? How could you win when they had muskets and cannons?"

"They never expected a few arrows to cause so much trouble." Grandma handed the quiver to Hess. "I daresay the British didn't believe that ladies were patriotic enough, smart enough, or brave enough to be a threat. They were foolish to underestimate me!"

Chapter 2

Hess forgot about her sampler as she looked at the design on the quiver. How, she wondered, had her grandma fought the British with arrows?

"In May of 1780, the British captured Charleston and the generals used our town house for their headquarters," said Grandma. "Later, they took our plantation house on the Congaree River and turn it into Fort Motte.

"If we lost the war, the British would get to keep all my property. When I had the chance to help our soldiers drive the British out of Fort Motte, I was happy to oblige. Do you want me to tell you the whole story?"

"Yes, we do!" Mary answered for both girls.

"Very well." Grandma paused to take a sip of lemonade. "For over one hundred and fifty years, England ruled the American colonies.

"When our citizens decided to form their own country, choose their leaders, and make their own laws, King George the Third used force to try to crush the colonists' plans.

"King George wanted to keep the colonies. He didn't want Americans to sell our lumber, tobacco, and other crops to any country but England. He wanted us to pay taxes on the things we bought from English merchants."

Hess knew her family's plantations made money by selling the rice, indigo, and cotton they grew. "Can Father and Uncle Thomas sell their crops to anyone they please?"

Grandma answered, "Yes, of course. The United States trades with many countries. Back then, people in Charleston protested the king's new tax on paper, which included the stamps used at the harbor to clear incoming and outgoing ships.

"But of all the taxes, the one on tea became a symbol of the disagreement between Britain and the colonies. Most patriots stopped buying tea and refused to drink it. Harbors in many cities refused to let tea from British merchants come ashore.

"In Charleston, folks refused 257 chests of tea that arrived on an East India Company ship named the *London*. In Boston, colonists went one step further and dumped hundreds of crates of tea into their harbor!"

"Oh my! That made the King angry, didn't it?" Mary put down her sampler and gave Grandma her full attention.

"It certainly did. After the trouble with the tea, King George sent thousands of soldiers to America. Those soldiers believed Americans were cowardly, inexperienced fighters who would surrender when they saw the Redcoats coming."

"The Americans didn't surrender," said Hess. "I know they didn't, because we won the war!"

"That's right. After four years of fighting, the British were no closer to stopping the rebellion in the north—and then France, who was Great Britain's enemy, joined the war on America's side.

"The British generals gave up on trying to conquer the northern states and sent troops down the coast to attack Georgia and the Carolinas."

"But why?" asked Hess. "The southern states hadn't picked a fight—except maybe when Charleston refused the tea."

"By that time, all the colonies were involved. The British officers believed there were enough people in the south who were loyal to the king, who would rise up and help the soldiers crush the rebellion."

Mary asked, "Grandma, how did you know who the patriots were and who was loyal to the king?"

"That's a good question. It wasn't easy to tell. Some people kept their opinions about the war a secret. Some people changed sides whenever it looked like one army was going to win."

Hess asked, "But people knew you were a patriot, didn't they?"

"In the first years of the war, I didn't keep my feelings a secret. Your Grandpa Jacob and I donated money and food to the army and sent some of our servants to help build up the city's defenses.

"Charleston was the largest, richest city south of Philadelphia. If it was captured by the British, it could end the war. The first two times they attacked Charleston, we fought them off. When they attacked a third time, thousands of American soldiers were waiting inside the city walls, ready to fight them off."

Chapter 3

Grandma paused when Ruth and Flora, two of the kitchen maids, came out to the porch. Ruth asked, "Miz Rebecca, do you want your dinner served here?"

"Yes, please," said Grandma. "That would be very nice."

The maids went to work. Ruth moved the low tea table out of the way and Flora set a larger table in front of Grandma. Flora laid out the knives, spoons, and napkins, Ruth placed covered dishes on the table, and then Hess and Mary moved their chairs to their places.

Hess felt her stomach rumble as Grandma said grace. Flora took away the dish covers, and Hess sniffed the rich aroma in the steam that rose from her plate. "Oh, I love shrimp pilau!"

In South Carolina, people ate rice at every meal, and the cooks at Eldorado knew dozens of delicious ways to prepare it. Spicy shrimp pilau was one of Hess's favorites.

A big platter in the middle of the table held several kinds of fruit and cheese, benne wafers sprinkled with sesame seeds, and butter and jam to spread on slices of warm, fragrant bread.

Grandma put her napkin on her lap. "Thank you, Ruth and Flora. That will be all."

The maids curtsied and went inside.

Hess savored her first bit of the pilau, and Mary buttered a slice of bread as Grandma continued her story.

"The British took Savannah late in 1778. When combined Americans and French forces failed to drive the British out, our General Lincoln and his troops marched to Charleston. More troops arrived through the winter, until the whole southern branch of the army and some militia units were inside the city."

Mary asked, "What did the Americans do to keep the British out of Charleston?"

"You can't see the defenses anymore," said Grandma, "but the soldiers built a wall with a gate on the northern edge of the city. They flooded a deep canal with water, added rows of felled trees with sharpened trunks and branches, and dug a ditch in front of the wall that they lined with pointed sticks. The British would have to get through all of those obstacles while under fire from the American soldiers."

Hess thought she would like to try to get through those defenses—except without any soldiers trying to stop her.

Grandma went on. "In the winter of 1779, the British landed on the sea islands outside the city. Their soldiers raided people's homes and took their food and supplies. They destroyed their furniture and dishes and stole their jewelry, clothes, sheets, and towels. They drove away their livestock and burned their houses and barns."

"That's no way to win the people's trust!" exclaimed Mary. "Why did they do that?"

"Perhaps fighting and destroying property made sense to the soldiers. But those attacks caused more people than ever to support the American cause.

"With the British patrols stirring up trouble all over the islands, many people fled from their plantations to the city, where there were American soldiers to protect them. Some of the people who lived in Charleston were afraid to stay where there was sure to be fighting. They packed up and left, hoping to find a safe place in the country."

Hess asked, "Where did you live then, Grandma?"

"We moved to our house on King Street just before the British attacked Charleston in 1776. I wanted to be nearby while your Grandpa Jacob was fighting in the militia. After he died in January 1780, I stayed in the city with your mothers and your Aunt Betsy and hoped for the best. If I had known what was going to happen, I might have made a different choice."

"What happened?" Mary and Hess spoke at the same time.

"General Clinton arrived in March with about 13,000 soldiers, which was many, many more than we had. They surrounded the city, and their ships blocked the harbor and the river so none of our ships could get in or out.

"The British soldiers put up earthworks and dug trenches so they could move closer to our defenses. Some of our soldiers took places on the wall with their rifles while others readied the cannons. The two armies traded fire, and the siege was underway."

"How is a siege different from a battle?" asked Hess.

"A battle takes place on open ground, or any place where both armies have room to retreat. When an enemy surrounds a town or building and cuts off supplies until the people inside surrender, that is a siege."

"That sounds lots worse than a battle," said Mary.

"Imagine Charleston, crowded with thousands of soldiers. Those soldiers, plus hundreds of refugees who had fled their homes, knocked on people's doors nearly every day to ask for food. By mid-April, everyone's supplies ran low."

Hess and Mary looked at each other in shock. Hess looked at the food left on their plates and the platter as Mary asked, "You really couldn't get anything to eat?"

"When we're in the city, we buy meat, eggs, vegetables, and fruit at the market, but the siege kept farmers from bringing in food to sell. It was too early in the year to harvest anything from the small vegetable plots and fruit trees in our city gardens.

"Shells rumbled like thunder as they exploded all over town, damaging homes and businesses. Terrified people ran for cover. Some of them were hurt, and some were killed.

"As the weeks went by, we grew used to the gunfire and the exploding shells, but we never got used to being hungry.

"I couldn't believe that just the year before I had given thousands of dollars' worth of rice and meat to the army, and now I didn't know how I would feed my family."

"How long did the siege last?" Hess asked.

Grandma smiled sadly. "It lasted six weeks, until May 12th. The British soldiers drained the canal and advanced until they were almost at the city wall. We could not sleep, and never had a moment's peace as they shelled the city all night and all day. The army was prepared to keep fighting, but in the end the citizens asked General Lincoln to surrender."

Chapter 4

Grandma touched her napkin to her lips, folded it, and put it beside her plate, the signal for Ruth and Flora to clear the table. The maids came forward as she went on with her story. "Charleston became the British army's base of operations in the south."

"Wait a minute, Grandma," said Hess. "You said that if the British captured Charleston, it could end the war. But it didn't, did it?"

"You've been paying attention, Hess!" Grandma looked pleased. "No, it didn't end the war, but it left the people of South Carolina discouraged. When word of the surrender got out, many back country towns surrendered too. Soon the British controlled South Carolina."

Mary asked, "Were you frightened with the British in charge? What about our mothers—were they afraid?"

"At first they treated us well, because they expected us to take an oath of loyalty to the King.

Your mothers were too young to take the oath, and I did my best to keep them away from the British soldiers and keep their lives as normal as possible.

"Some people who supported King George were happy to take the oath. Others who claimed to be patriots before the siege did too. The true rebels refused. Many ladies wore all black for two years to mourn the city's defeat!"

Hess asked, "Did you wear mourning for the city?"

"Even though my heart was full of sorrow, it was time to keep my feelings to myself. I had to because General Henry Clinton, the commander of the British army, chose my house for his headquarters."

"Oh, my!" said Hess. "Couldn't you say no?"

"I can't imagine a British general living in your house," said Mary.

"There was nothing I could do. General Clinton and his aides moved in. Soldiers came and went from headquarters at all hours, bringing messages and discussing plans.

"The general expected me to eat dinner with thirty officers every night. Sometimes they made fun of the American army in my hearing.

"One of them, Captain McPherson, was especially rude. He said, 'Missus Motte, you cannot imagine how pleased I am to see Charleston's leading citizens brought low. I think you can see that there is nothing to gain, and everything to lose, by supporting the American side.'"

The very thought of someone being rude to Grandma made Hess angry. "I wish the American soldiers could've helped you."

"Even though I was a patriot, I pretended I wasn't interested in the Cause in front of my houseguests. If they knew how I really felt, it would've ruined my plan to help our soldiers!"

Chapter 5

When the lunch dishes were cleared away, Grandma picked up her knitting again. "The American prisoners were tired from fighting. Their uniforms were in tatters. Many were sick or wounded, and there weren't enough army doctors to attend to them. The British kept them under guard in the barracks or on prison ships and gave them small portions of the worst food. We ladies helped by bringing them food, medicine, and clothes, and trying to cheer them up."

"General Francis Marion, who was a family friend, escaped capture because he was recovering from a broken ankle at his home during the siege. After the surrender, Marion was the only American officer in the area who could oppose the British. He gathered a group of farmers, natives, former slaves, and some soldiers who had escaped from Charleston.

"Marion's Men hid in the swamps in small groups and disrupted the British supply and communication lines with surprise, hit-and-run attacks, and then disappeared. This forced Lord Cornwallis to send extra soldiers to protect his convoys, which weakened his main force in Charleston and made it easier for more prisoners to escape."

"General Marion sent his servants through the lines to run errands in town. While they were there, they spoke to other servants at the market and learned who might be able to observe the British and give messages to his servants. Once he knew I was in a position to help—"

Hess's eyes grew round. "Grandma, were you a spy?"

"I thought of myself as an observer, but I suppose I was!"

"You were?" shouted Hess. "Really?"

"It was my duty as a patriot. The British officers did not expect women to understand politics or have opinions—or to be able to keep a secret, for that matter!

"The officers were careless around my servants. When the maids brought in refreshments or firewood, the officers spoke in front of them as if they did not understand English."

"My goodness!" said Hess. "What if you got caught observing?"

"I knew I was risking my life to gather information, just as soldiers risked their lives in battle. I did what I could to help, and the British never suspected a thing.

"The attacks from Marion's Men cut off communications between Charleston and Camden. In time, the British lost their hold on the southern states."

"When I heard a rumor that the British would take the homes of patriots that refused the loyalty oath and make them leave Charleston, I decided it was time to move to our plantation on the Santee River.

"We had always lived in town during the summer and fall months to avoid the threat of malaria and yellow fever that rose from the swamps in the country.

"Your Aunt Betsy had married a Continental officer a few months before the siege began, and she was going to have a baby very soon. Our home in the country was the best place to keep my daughters safe and healthy."

Chapter 6

Grandma paused to take another sip of lemonade. "My, talking so much makes me thirsty! Perhaps we should finish this story another day."

"No, please go on!" said Hess.

"We have to know what happens next," said Mary.

"I asked for a pass for my family and servants to leave the city and travel to Mount Joseph. We packed a few things, and I left my house, furniture, silver, and dishes in the hands of the enemy. As we rode out of the city, I prayed there would be no soldiers where we were going."

"Grandma, did you take the quiver and the arrows?" asked Mary.

"Oh! I almost forgot about the arrows!" said Hess.

"Yes, I did bring the arrows and quiver. My brother had prized them, and I didn't want to leave them behind for the British to destroy."

"When we arrived at Mount Joseph, I noticed that the house at Belleview, our neighbor's plantation, had been turned into a fort. It was full of British soldiers. Would I never be rid of them?

"Betsy's baby, your cousin Thomas, was born in August. Within days, we learned that her husband was shot in the leg and taken prisoner at the Battle of Camden. His wound did not heal well, and he nearly died from the infection. It was months before he was paroled and allowed to come to Mount Joseph where we could take care of him.

"We found it hard to be merry at Christmas, and the new year was no better. Betsy's husband received orders to report to Philadelphia and await exchange. Betsy and little Thomas went with him. Your mothers and I remained at Mt. Joseph with some of our servants."

"Were you lonely?" asked Mary.

"No, because one morning I woke to a loud crash. From the window, I watched as soldiers cut down my trees, dug a large ditch around the house, and mounded up earthworks. Over the next few months, they built a tall fence around the house with wooden towers on the corners for the soldiers on lookout. Then they cut down more trees and placed the sharpened trunks in front of the earthworks.

"When the fort was finished in April, Captain McPherson and one hundred and fifty soldiers moved in. They raised the British flag over the house, and Captain McPherson named it Fort Motte. Your mothers, the servants, and I had to stay in a few of the upstairs rooms. Every other corner of the house was filled with soldiers."

"After a month, Captain McPherson ordered us to pack up immediately and move to an empty house nearby. We didn't know why we were being sent away, but we obeyed orders."

Grandma picked up the quiver and held it on her lap.

"This quiver had come from Charleston with me, and I didn't want to leave it behind for the soldiers to destroy. When we were ready to go, I slung the strap over my shoulder. Captain McPherson stopped me at the gate."

"Did he try to take the arrows?" asked Hess.

Grandma laughed. "He said, 'What have you got here, Missus Motte?'" He pulled out an arrow and touched his finger to the point.

"'Be careful, Captain,'" I said. "'Those arrows are poisoned.'

"He wasn't sure whether to believe me. Then he scoffed and handed the arrow back. He said, 'I suppose a woman can't do much harm with a few arrows—poisoned or not.'

"Some of the soldiers laughed as I walked away. I didn't want to admit it, but Captain McPherson was right. A handful of arrows couldn't do much against that many soldiers.

"Our new house sat high on a ridge. From our front yard we could see inside the fort. The soldiers moving about looked ants on a giant anthill. They were getting ready for something —but what?"

"What was it? What happened next?" asked Mary.

"We didn't know it yet, but General Greene, who commanded the southern branch of the Continental army, had sent some troops to capture the British forts along the Congaree River. They were on their way to attack Fort Motte!"

Chapter 7

Hess was so excited she bounced in her chair and almost spilled her lemonade.

"The next day," Grandma said, "General Francis Marion and Colonel Henry Lee arrived with three hundred soldiers and a cannon."

"Huzzah!" said Hess.

"You could help General Marion again!" said Mary. "Did you tell him and Colonel Lee how many soldiers were in the fort?"

"Yes, I certainly did! I also told them about the house and the grounds, and how the soldiers were crowded inside.

"I offered my home for their headquarters, and I was so happy to be hosting my friends instead of the enemy. That evening we served the officers a delicious meal and our finest wine.

"Then what did the soldiers do?" asked Hess.

"After supper, the officers held a war council. They decided to give Captain McPherson a chance to surrender before they attacked. The next morning, McPherson refused the offer and told his men to prepare to defend the fort.

"Colonel Lee organized his men into groups to dig trenches for cover. General Marion's sharpshooters took up positions out of range of the British muskets and fired at any Redcoat who tried to shoot at Colonel Lee's men. A third group of soldiers moved the cannon up on a hill so they could fire down into the fort."

"I wonder if Captain McPherson was sorry he made you leave the fort," said Mary.

"I didn't think of that!" said Hess. "He probably didn't realize you could help General Marion and Colonel Lee—that is, until it was too late."

"That's true, girls. This time, I was on the other side of the siege, wasn't I? On the third day of fighting, General Greene's courier galloped up with a message for General Marion. His scouts had seen the British Colonel Lord Rawdon's troops heading this way. Those reinforcements would arrive in the next day or two.

"That night we saw the glow of Lord Rawdon's campfires in the distance. The fighting began again in the morning, and the British did not budge.

"Just before noon Colonel Lee came to me, his hat in his hand. He looked so serious that I asked, 'Why, Colonel, what is the matter?'

"'Mrs. Motte,' he said, 'we must force a surrender before Lord Rawdon arrives, and we can think of only one way that is fast enough. Will you give us permission to set your house on fire?'"

Both Hess and Mary gasped, and Hess asked, "What did you say?"

"Poor Colonel Lee! He felt so awful. I think he was more upset than I was!

"'Don't worry,' I said. 'You may burn the house. It won't make me sad. In fact, I shall view the scene with delight.'

"General Marion gave Captain McPherson one last chance to surrender. He refused, and said he would fight to the last man."

Mary asked, "McPherson knew Lord Rawdon's men would be there soon, didn't he?"

"Yes he did, but poor Captain McPherson was about to get a big surprise. No one, not even the American generals, knew what I was about to suggest."

Chapter 8

Grandma set the quiver aside and took another sip of lemonade.

"General Marion joined Colonel Lee and me in the house. He started to apologize, but I stopped him. 'We should move quickly. Let me help you start the blaze.' I took the quiver of arrows off its peg on the wall. 'These belonged to my brother.' I couldn't help laughing. 'I told Captain McPherson they were poisoned, but in truth, they will light on fire when they are launched. Perhaps your soldiers could shoot them onto the roof?'

"General Marion rubbed his hands together in delight. 'That's quite a plan, Mrs. Motte—and it will surprise Captain McPherson. Let's get to work.'

"One of the soldiers wrapped little piles of gunpowder in paper, twisted them closed and tied them behind the arrowheads. Then he covered the paper with cloth and sealed it with pine resin. He said, 'When the fire burns through the outer layers, the gunpowder will explode.'

"The shingle roof was dried out by the scorching sun. It would catch fire easily. Colonel Lee chose Private Nathan Savage, one of his best marksmen, to fire the first arrow. Private Savage put an arrow in the barrel of his musket, took aim, and fired.

"The arrow flew through the air and stuck fast on the roof. We heard the gunpowder go off. General Marion looked through his spyglass. 'I see smoke—and now a flame!'"

"Oh, my goodness!" exclaimed Hess.

"It was so exciting, I wanted to cheer. None of the soldiers inside the fort knew what was happening.

"Private Savage fired twice more, and soon we could see the flames without a spyglass. Smoke rolled into the sky. Then an alarm sounded inside the fort."

"What did they do?" asked Mary.

"Some of the soldiers tried to climb onto the roof, but Colonel Lee's men fired the cannon and sent them scrambling for cover. The American sharpshooters fired every time someone tried to put out the blaze.

"The flames spread until the whole roof was aflame. Captain McPherson knew they were trapped. He raised a white flag. The British soldiers threw open the gates, hurried out of the fort, dropped their guns on the ground, and raised their hands.

When the fort was empty, Colonel Lee sent his men inside to put out the fire.

"Did the whole house burn down?"

"No. Thankfully it all happened so quickly that only the roof was damaged. General Marion and Colonel Lee accepted McPherson's surrender, and claimed the ammunition, food, and supplies stored in the fort."

"Huzzah!" shouted Hess as Mary clapped her hands.

"With the prisoners under guard, McPherson and his officers joined Marion and Lee at my farmhouse, where we had dinner together. I had something I wanted to say to Captain McPherson."

You did?" said Mary.

"I raised a toast and thanked him for doing his part for the American cause!"

They all laughed.

Grandma said, "I couldn't resist being saucy. It may have been the most satisfying dinner party I ever hosted. It was May 12, 1781, exactly one year after Charleston fell to the British."

Hess threw her arms around Grandma and gave her a big hug. "It's all right for a proper lady to be saucy sometimes."

"It certainly is!" Grandma straightened Hess's crooked flower crown.

Mary asked, "What happened to Fort Motte?"

"The American troops tore down the towers and the fence and filled in the trench. Soon it looked like a house again. And that is the story of the Siege of Fort Motte!

"There were many battles more costly and bloody, but that victory was a link in the chain of events that ended British control of South Carolina.

Grandma said proudly, "Lots of regular people like me helped win the American Revolution by being courageous enough to do the unexpected!"

Author's Note

All the characters in this story were real people.

Rebecca Brewton Motte (1737-1815) grew up in Charleston, where her father was a successful goldsmith and banker. Her older brother, Miles, was a planter and businessman who was chosen as a delegate to the Second Continental Congress in 1775. He decided to take his wife and children with him to Philadelphia, but tragedy struck when their ship was lost in a storm off Cape Hatteras, leaving no survivors.

After the deaths of Miles and his family, Rebecca inherited his plantation on the Congaree River and his townhouse at 27 King Street. When Rebecca's husband Jacob died in 1780, she inherited his property as well. At the age of 42, she was perhaps the wealthiest woman in South Carolina.

Though Rebecca had a great deal to lose, she did not hesitate to sacrifice what she had for the good of the patriot cause.

Hess and Mary

Rebecca and Jacob Motte called their youngest daughter Mary by the nickname "Hess." When the first Hess grew up, married, and had a family of her own, she named her youngest daughter Mary and called her by the same nickname. She is the Hess in our story.

I did not learn where the nickname Hess came from, but I am sure it was used to distinguish her from several girls named Mary in their large family.

Mary Pinkney died at age 17. While I could not confirm her cause of death, many people who lived in the low country in this time died from diseases that are treatable today. In the 1700s, average life expectancies in the southern colonies were 10-20 years less than in the northern colonies.

The House on King Street

The Miles Brewton House, located at 27 King Street, was built around 1769. It is a designated National Historic Landmark and is on the National Register of Historic Places.

Captain William Alston, who married Rebecca's daughter Mary (the first Hess) purchased the house for his family's town residence. The second Hess lived there while she was growing up.

Years later, when the second Hess was grown up and married to a man named William Pringle, she inherited the house and lived there until her death in 1884, at the age of 81. That is why some people in Charleston know it as the Pringle House.

The Pringle House was used as a Union army headquarters during the federal occupation of Charleston in 1865. I am sure Hess recalled her grandmother's stories about the Revolution when she found herself in the same position— forced to endure unwelcome soldiers living under her roof.

Rebecca's descendants still own and live in the house.

Slavery

Slavery was legal in the United States during the American Revolution. The Motte, Brewton, and Pinkney families were like many others who had enslaved people to do the work at their plantations and houses.

Just because something is legal does not make it right. America's fight for liberty caused many people to rethink their opinion of slavery, and slavery was abolished in the United States after the Civil War.

Slavery was part of the world Hess was born into, but as an adult, she developed strong feelings against slavery, which was an unusual point of view for the wife and daughter of slaveholders.

In the more difficult language of the day, Hess wrote that "slavery, of itself, is revolting enough to every Christian and humane bosom, and does not require the aid of misrepresentation to render it more distressing...[but] it cannot be done away with."

Hess disagreed with the ministers at the Protestant Episcopal church she attended, because they gave approval to the practice of enslaving others. She wrote that she found their attitude "morally reprehensible."

You can learn more about Mary Alston Pringle and her life by reading *Mary's World: Love, War, and Family Ties in Nineteenth-century Charleston* by Richard N. Cote.

When we learn about history, we encounter good and bad things. It is our job, as curious students and historians, to examine what happened, recognize the bad parts, and commit ourselves to making sure the bad things never happen again.

Rebecca Motte and her family lived long before computers, television, radio, and telephones were invented. In their lifetimes, people kept journals. They sent letters to share news. Sometimes they wrote books or pamphlets, or had articles published in newspapers.

Those writings were not usually about women, but the story of Rebecca's special arrows and the attack on Fort Motte can be found in many books and articles.

Most women's stories were kept alive within families. They were told around the fireside as entertainment and passed down from generation to generation.

While researching this book, I learned a lot about what happened after the British captured the city of Charleston, and I found plenty of information about Rebecca and the events of her life.

However, there was no way to know everything she might have done or said. Sometimes I had to use my imagination, and that's why this type of story is called historical fiction. It blends things that really happened with things the author made up.

Women played a vital role in the fight for America's independence from Great Britain. There are lots more stories about women heroes of the Revolution yet to be discovered!

About the DAR

The National Society Daughters of the American Revolution was founded in 1890 with the simple mission of promoting historic preservation, education and patriotism.

Any woman 18 years or older, regardless of race, religion, or ethnic background, who can prove lineal descent from a patriot of the American Revolution, is eligible to join.

Learn more at https://dar.org

About the Author

Tracy Lawson wanted to be an author since she was a little girl. For most of her adult life, she worked as a dance teacher and a choreographer in educational theater. *Revolutionary Sarah* is her twelfth book, and the second written for young readers. Tracy and her husband live in Wylie, TX. They have one grown daughter.

About the Illustrator

When Larissa Coriell was a little girl, she took dancing lessons from Tracy, and they have been friends ever since! Larissa graduated from Columbus College of Art and Design and has worked as a costume designer and freelance artist. She and her husband live near Pittsburgh.

Other books in the
Liberty Belles Series:

Revolutionary Anna

Revolutionary Sarah

Answering Liberty's Call: Anna Stone's Daring Ride to Valley Forge, is another of Tracy's books about women in the American Revolution, written for adult readers.

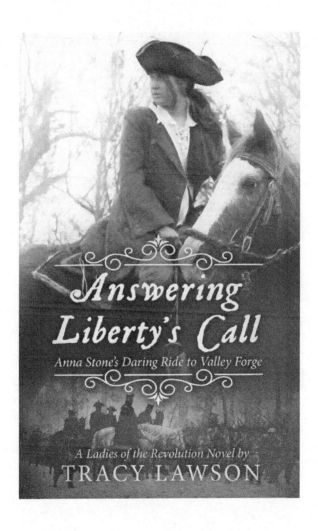

Made in the USA
Monee, IL
13 November 2024

70004297R00038